SOMETHING LIKE MAGIC

ON REMEMBERING HOW TO BE ALIVE

ISBN 978-0-9981490-2-8

Flying Edna
P.O. Box 201
East Sandwich, MA 02537
USA

kai@flyingedna.com
fia@flyingedna.com
flyingedna.com

Revised Edition: January, 2022

To you, my readers, who have followed the stories over the years. From countless conversations with you, I think it's clear by now: these were never my stories alone. You remind me daily with your own stories of love & gratitude & heartache & loss that I have the great privilege of telling all of our stories. I thank you for the gift of that...

Other books by Kai Skye (under the pen name Brian Andreas):

Mostly True
Still Mostly True
Going Somewhere Soon
Strange Dreams
Hearing Voices
Story People
Trusting Soul
Traveling Light
Some Kind of Ride
Peculiar Times (e-book)
Theories of Everything
Something Like Magic
Impossible to Know
Bring Your Life Back to Life
Songs of Starlight

With Fia Skye:

Creative Anarchy
Everyday Angels

With Lorne Resnick:

Cuba: This Moment Exactly So

SOMETHING LIKE MAGIC

ON REMEMBERING
HOW TO BE ALIVE

Love & Secrets

Not too long ago, I was at a sprawling party with a lot of people I didn't know. Halfway through the night, I found myself a quiet place on a bench in the garden. I'd only been there for a couple of minutes when a woman came down the path & sat at the far end of the bench. We nodded at each other. Neither of us spoke. We sat in the dusk together & listened to the cricket songs & thought our own private thoughts. After awhile, she stood up. Sometimes, she said, you just need to remember the most important thing. Then she smiled & made her way back to the party.

Long after she left, her words floated quietly in the dark. It felt like she had given me something precious in those words: you just need to remember the most important thing.

She didn't say find the most important thing. Or make a list with the most important thing at the top. Or ask someone else what they think is the most important thing. No, it was much, much simpler than that. It was remember the most important thing.

Because we already know what the most important thing is. Our work here is to remember...

When I finally showed this to a few friends, I prefaced it by saying that this was a book filled with love & secrets. Of course it's about love, they said, that's what you do. But what about the secrets? How will we know where the secrets are?

Oh, you'll know, I said. They all start with the word 'secret'.

Which is very funny. Because that's not how most secrets work. Most secrets are secret because not everybody knows them. These secrets are different, though. These are secret because a lot of us know them & along the way, a lot of us forgot.

That's exactly why I call them secrets. Each one is something like magic, because all it takes it a moment of remembering them & suddenly the whole world sparkles again. The funny thing is it never stopped sparkling. We just stopped seeing it, because it was too simple & we were convinced it must be something different. We let ourselves be convinced the most important thing was something different than the love & magic that's been here all along.

I sat in the garden that night & I thought about the most important thing for me. That we love & are loved. All the time, in every moment, no matter how it looks to other eyes that don't remember quite yet. That's why I think remembering is one of the most important things we can do right now. It's how we stop & see the world again for the very first time. In all of its aching beauty & joy & pain. The immensity of all of it. It's how we open to being loved wildly & deliciously until we are filled beyond anything we ever thought we could hold.

I hope the stories here are a reminder to you. A reminder to stop & see the world again for the very first time. When you do & one day not long after, your most important thing ripples through you like an immense wave of light, I hope you'll see why I say it's something like magic. Because you'll see it's been there all along in the heart of you, waiting for you to remember you're alive now & everything you are is Love.

But, like I said, you already know that...

with all my love,

Kai Skye
Cape Cod, Massachusetts
January 17, 2022

Start Here

I see you doubt the parts of you
that love the world so much
you wonder if you'll ever
be able to show it

I want to take your face in
my hands & say, You who love
the world so much?

That's what you are here to do.

Secret #1:

Every single moment say Yes to Life (& don't be afraid to say No in order to do that.)

Remember You're Making a World Today !!! ⭐

Unicorn Life

Today, after some reflection,
I decided I'm never going to
pretend I know anything
about Life ever again, other
than there's a word for it.

Like there's a word for unicorn,
though no one has ever seen one,
except from far away & maybe
it was just a trick of the light.

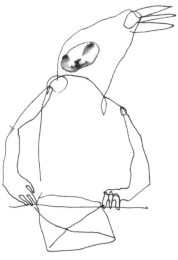

The Point

This is a pretty small space
to fit all the stuff I've been
thinking lately, but it's also
a pretty good reminder to
get to the point.

Busy Work

At a certain point,
feeling afraid
is a bad habit
from when you thought
being afraid
would somehow
help.

Here's the thing
you should know:
it doesn't.

Feel free to stop
any time.

Two Paths

No matter what, you
always have two paths.
One where everyone
else goes

& the other you
discover yourself.

Usually some bruising
with the second one,
but it's a hell of a lot
more fun.

The Night We Were Stars

We sat in the dark, holding hands
& let the sky pull us up into
a million stars & it was quiet
for a long time & then you said
They're more beautiful tonight
than any stars I've seen before

& I could only nod & wonder if
this is how it always is when you
let yourself love enough to become
the world you see.

Simple Truth

Her whole life shifted the day
she started to tell the truth
about what made her happy.

I never knew it could be
so simple, she said.

It's not easy to explain to
those who don't see the WILD
in her, but every Day is like
Being born again into the wonder
of her strong HEART beating
& a full-throated KNOWING
that she's here to Be ALive.

WILD HEART

THE SOFT DARK

It still amazes me the way you love
so simply that it wraps around
both of us

& there are no words, except
for those moments in the soft
dark when you look in my eyes
& whisper, Hi

RESTART

The first time they met,
time stopped

& when it finally began
again, they laughed
with relief

because it wasn't too late
to have the whole rest
of their lives together.

Someone asked me about you the other day & I said something like she is NOT too TALL & her hair is such & such a color. I said THAT, because HOW could I tell them YOU are like the play of sunlight on WATER, dAncINg to music we don't often hear. Or the song of DoveS, like the soft sounds a WomaN makes when she is TRULY kissed. Or the way people smile at each other when there is nothing to HiDe. How could I tell them YoU are the way Love looks when it walks through this world of ours? How could I say that to them before I spent a Lifetime saying that to You?

LOVE LOOKS

Secret #2:

There is no RIGHT way to do LiFe. There's oNLy stuff that Works & STUFF That doesn't

BEGINNING WISDOM

Wisdom is one of those things
that when you finally have it,
it feels like common sense

But when you don't, it feels like
someone just trying to get you
to do what they want, but not
coming right out & saying it.

When this happens, just remember
they did not know either, when
they were then & not now.

This will not make it any easier,
since you'll go ahead not knowing,
saying things like What the hell.
Or What do they know?

Later on, when you get wise,
you will look back & see this
is how it begins, choosing
your own life, even this.

Stand Off

I don't worry about what
could go wrong.

I worry about whether
I'm in a place yet
where I could handle it

if everything goes right.

Quick Getaway

My heart says
Be bold. Jump in
with both feet.

But part of me
still wants to jump
in with one foot, so
I have the other
available for a
quick getaway.

In case my heart
picks something
I'm not ready for
yet.

I don't know who we'll BECOME in the days ahead. I only KNOW the QuieT Voice in my heart that says We'll become it together.

BEING TOGETHER

Best Love

I feel how you sit in stillness
& love the world with all you are

(because it is the same for me)

& still there is a part of me that
wants to hear your voice now
& then saying, You are the one
I love best of all.

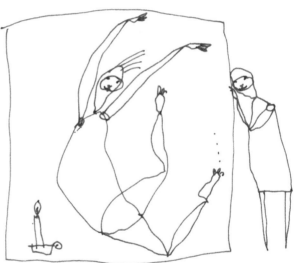

Fair Use

You'll forget & then
remember & then
forget again

& it's not so bad,
as long as you remember
it doesn't matter
if you forget,

because Life keeps
living through you
the whole time, no
matter what you do.

HOW TO LIVE A LIFE
(OR at least what
I know so far...)

1. You already are. Now, when are you going to choose to enjoy it?

(How's that for clearing up the clutter?)

Secret #3:

They say there's only love or Fear, but there's really only Love. Sometimes it takes being afraid awhile to see that.

Love Matters

Someone once told me that people will do anything
for love & I had a hard time believing that because
there's Love everywhere. In the sunlight & air & trees
& rocks. In the way words attach themselves to the
things we do & see. In the heartbeat (beat beat beat)
of the world.

They told me that didn't count. Love only counts
if you get it from other people, they said.

I looked around & all I could see were people wanting
love, but not wanting to give it because it might hurt.
Or because someone might say Go away. Take your Love
& go someplace else where people actually want it
(which is silly, because that's everywhere)

It still makes me wonder if the only reason
people will do anything for Love is because
they think there's only a little bit

& not the whole world.

Two Conversations

I.

I was sitting here wondering
what I would say if you were
here next to me,

until I figured out it wouldn't
really matter, as long as you
were here next to me.

II.

You, who wonders when
someone will love you
the way you know you
will love them back.

Stop wondering.

I am one who loves you
that way. Even if you
don't see it yet.

LEARNING TO LOVE

I see you walking slowly
through the world, learning
to love everything again
for the first time.

I want to hold you & say
exactly the words you need
to hear, because I have been
there, too

& I know the courage
it takes to go on when
your every breath aches.

READY WHEN YOU ARE

My idea of when
I should be ready
& my actual readiness
are different enough
that a good part of
my day is spent
calming down.

LITTLE HELP

This morning, in
the stillness, I heard
a small voice say,
Trust love

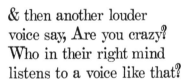

& then another louder
voice say, Are you crazy?
Who in their right mind
listens to a voice like that?

I had to laugh & agree
because I've already
trusted love for a very
long time

& I don't really need
a voice to know that.

When you start to CRACK OPeN, don't waste a MOment gathering your Old self up into Something like you knew BeFORe. Let your New Self SpLASH like sunlight into every dark place & Laugh & Cry & make Sounds you Never Made & thANK ALL that is holy for the gift, because Now you Have No Choice but to let all YouR Love spill Out into the world.

THE GIFT OF YOU

Secret #4:

You leARn how to
Do LiFe by doing it.
You learn more slowly
if you think you can
SKiP this part.

TRANSPARENT

How do I explain the softness
that comes when your skin
no longer stands between you
& things you learned were not
you, when your skin no longer
holds so tightly to the idea of
separation?

Perhaps it's the way the line
between earth & sea is nothing
real, but always becoming one,
or the other, at your feet. You
stand exactly there in the morning
fog & the sound of gulls drops like
rain upon the sand

& it seems strange, in moments
like these, with the sound of waves
beating like my own heart outside
my skin, that the idea of separation
is ever enough to make us forget.

Stock Parts

I used to spend more time
sorting out which part was me
& which part was the stuff
I learned so I could fit in.

Until I figured out the part
that's most me is the part
that's so excited to be alive
I can barely breathe

& the part that wonders
if it's OK to be here, or
if I'm doing it right, well,
I'm better off if I just
ignore it.

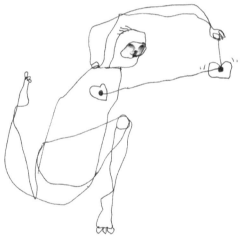

Voices

Stop listening to the voices
that tell you not to trust
your own heart to be alive.

They are not on your side.

(Unlike this voice here.)

First Dance

I never imagined that first
time I danced with you
would bring me here,

to this exact moment, where
everything I do, even sitting
quietly breathing

is a dance with you.

This Life

Today there is such
stillness & gratitude
for this life that
pays no attention
to what I think
I want.

Good Talk

The other day, someone asked me
to explain Love to them. They said
I looked like someone who knew
what they were talking about
when it came to love.

Later, when I got home, I looked
in the mirror because I wanted to see
how they could tell.

I looked about how I usually do.

All of a sudden, she came in & said
What the hell are you doing? & when
I told her, she started laughing
so hard she couldn't breathe,

because we can't even explain love to
each other, much less to someone who
thinks it's something you find words for
in the first place.

To tell you the truth, I'm not a lot
of help talking about Love, but
I'll do my best to love you while
you figure it out on your own.

Boss

I know it's time to go
off by myself for awhile
when I start thinking
You are not the boss of me

even to my own self.

Delight

The whole time
you've known me
I've been delighted
by the world,

so I think it's easy
for you to miss that
you're my favorite
part of that.

Outside Voice

A lot of stuff changes once you figure out
the voices you hear in your head have
no idea what they're talking about.

If they knew anything at all about
the world, they'd stop in amazement

because why waste all that time
talking when you could be spinning
around & around laughing &
soaking it all in?

LIFE BALANCE

still trying to balance a life
filled with laughter & wonder
& love,

knowing that kind of life
is going to baffle most
everyone she meets

SOFT SKIN

I am still wrapped in
your soft skin today

& is it any wonder
that all I can do is
sit here without words,

smiling with the joy
of being in this world
with you.

secret # 5:

imaginE something
that gives you joy.
got it ? Now go &
  be Like that All day
            Long

(Yes. It is that simple...)

Once, there was a Girl who
wanted to CHANGe the
world & at first, she thought it'd
BE EaSY, because if everyOne
could see how BEAUTIFUL it'd be,
it'd take ABOUT A
MINUte. But all the people
she talked to were TOO busy busy
busy BUSY
to Stop & Listen. So, she went OFF &
did BeAUTiFul Things all on heR OWN
& pretty Soon People were stopping & asking
if they CoulD coMe Along & DO THAt, too
& that's how SHe figured out how worlds
CHange.

BEAUTIFUL THINGS

TIME & SPACE

There are moments lately when
I look up & see you standing there,
perhaps with your eyes closed,
listening to the wind

& everything stops & I take
the sight of you gently in
my hands & put it in a safe
place in my heart & I know

exactly in that moment,
I'm alive with you &
here is exactly where
I want to be.

A Thousand Lifetimes

It's not something that's easy
to explain, to see you standing
there, etched in the morning
light & suddenly remember
every one of a thousand
lifetimes with you

& at the same time, this one
exquisite life that will never
be enough to know you
all over again.

Slightly Less

I gave you my slightly less
than perfect heart &

you said it was exactly
the kind of heart
you'd always hoped
would love
your heart
back.

Come Before

There will come a moment in your life
when you look into the future & wonder
if the way you love the world matters

& almost without thinking, you'll want
to find someone who already answered
this question you never thought to ask.

It's hard to believe, but the ones who came
before hope you come to this.

You'll look in their eyes & see what they
could not speak (& even if they could,
you would not have heard until now),
because how do you say I remember,
when so many people shake their heads
& say Remember what?

But in the moment when you see again
who we all are, everything changes
& you'll love the world differently
because of that & I promise
for the ones who come after,
the ones you may never
know, it matters.

Universal Laws

I have a theory that once upon a time
the whole universe was smaller than
a grain of sand & then someone found
it & loved it & wondered what it could
become & it opened up in a thousand
directions all at once

& my friend who does physics said
Science calls that the Big Bang &
they think that's how universes are
made

& it makes me smile, since I see what
happens when people are loved &
it makes sense that Universes
wouldn't be much different.

Things You Might Want to Know About Magic

The most important thing to know is simple: magic is real.
There are lots of books out now that have magic in them. A lot
of people think they are fiction. Except when you read them,
something deep inside you stirs. Like a little spark or an ember.
Or a bright hummingbird that suddenly wakes & darts up into
the quiet dark & starts to hum.

Magic has been quietly waiting for a long time for us to stop
being so busy with our shiny things made of metal & glass &
wires & electricity. It has been waiting for us to wake up & see
that we're already where we always wanted to be. That we're
already home.

A lot of people get confused about Life because when they were
young, something happened that hurt. Maybe it was someone who
made fun of their hair. Or the color of their skin. Or the number
of freckles they had. Or they were too skinny. Or too fat.

But there are worse things than that when you are young. The
worst thing is when you have adults around you that forget that
children are there to remind us the magic is real, that innocence
is one of the things that's big enough to create the world all over
again every day, bigger & brighter every time. When you have
adults around you who forget that, they do mean & stupid things
that can hurt for your whole life.

When you have a hurt like that, it's easy to get confused about
Life because instead of playing the game called Trust Love &
Adventure & Magic, you start playing another game called Stop
the Hurt.

You start doing things that stop the hurt, like gathering people around you who would never, ever do anything that even reminds you of the hurt. Or worse, you start hurting other people first because hurt people leave you alone. That's the biggest problem with hurt: you think if you can get enough alone, the hurt will stop. Because it was people who made it hurt to begin with. Funny how that works. The only real way for hurt to stop is to be with people who hear you say It hurts & they hold you & kiss you & put Bactine & a band-aid on it & they maybe make you a grilled cheese sandwich with some animal crackers & they tell you the truth: everyone hurts sometimes because being alive is not an exact science & we bump into each other because we're not looking & we're so busy not looking that we miss the thing that's right in front of us the whole time: every human being on the planet, every dog & every cat, every cow & fish & flower, maybe even every rock & all the pieces of dust under your bed, everything is alive. Everything is here to love being alive & to love every other thing that's alive.

Have you ever seen the way a small child squats down in the grass & talks to the bugs & the twigs & the ants going about their own business? The way they'll dance & sing songs to the wind? If you could stop for even a minute from your busy & serious life & listen with every cell of your body, you would understand again every song that child is singing.

I say 'again' because you already know. You just forget for awhile. Try it. Stop for a minute. Not just any way of stopping, but a special way of stopping. Like this: close your eyes. (Oh, wait a minute. First, read all of this & then close your eyes. Otherwise, you'll have to keep opening them & it'll never work.)

When you finally do close your eyes, here's what you're NOT going to do:

1. You're not going to work hard at it.

2. You're not going to do it exactly like I say, because there's going to be someone who's going to show up to help you out. This could be a favorite relative, or a saint. Or Divine Mother. Or that old guy with the smiling eyes who sits outside of the liquor store who sees everything. Just welcome them & listen to what they say, because they're here to help. Follow them, because they know the shortcut. For you.

3. You're not going to watch your breathing. That's so boring & you'll just get frustrated & when you're frustrated, nothing happens. (Note: the reason nothing ever happens when you're frustrated is that you're so involved with being frustrated that you forget that what you're here to do is listen with every cell of your body.)

4. You're not going to argue with me. You're not going to tell me things like this'll never work. Or science has proven magic doesn't exist. Or you've done your own research. Or even something like How can you be so sure? I can be so sure, because I can do it & if you can't & you'd like to learn, it might make sense to stop arguing. If you want to argue, go right ahead. But don't mind me if I ignore you & go on filling my world with magic & love every moment of my life.

Here's what you ARE going to do. It's actually quite simple:

1. Close your eyes.

2. Remember your favorite place. This doesn't have to be
real. I have a favorite place that's a field of grass & a
mountain & a counter with an endless supply of treats
& there is always a breeze & sun & there are always one
or two friendly clouds. So, what's your favorite place?
What's it look like? What colors are there? What does it
smell like? What are you wearing? Really be there.

3. Now, listen. You'll hear something. Maybe a song in a
little girl's voice. Or a hum, like bees.

4. Whatever that sound is, I want you to let it slip inside
you until your bones start to vibrate with it.

5. When you are vibrating inside, almost like you are a
tuning fork, let your skin disappear so there is nothing
between you & the sound & your favorite place.

6. This is you all the time. This is the you that you forget.
This is the you that hears the music in raindrops &
the sound of sunlight & the secret whispers of the rocks
& trees. This is the you that has never forgotten that
magic is at the heart of the world.

7. Trust this. Start now. (Yeah, I know. This is often the
hardest thing. Simply starting. But it's not as hard as
not trusting it. The magic is in this exact moment. Go
& be joyful in it...)

SEcret #6:

Making PlanS for your life doesn't get you out of the stuff that comes along whenever it feels like it.

Step Right Up!!

The Door to the Mysteries

It's an old white house, with boards on the windows.
This cannot be, you think, but there it is, even to
the secret way inside, by the back stairs.

Hello, you say, is anybody here? hoping someone
answers, but already knowing there's only you,
in that long hall with its invitation of doors.

You walk slowly, pushing through the slow breathing
silence, until you stand before the last door.

You press against it & it sticks & for an instant you
think Oh well, I tried & then suddenly, it opens &
there's a familiar smell, maybe lavender, or old newspaper.
There's a photograph with faded ink that says With love
always, exactly like every other time you dreamed this
all the days of your life.

I can't say for sure what it'll be. It's different for everyone.

But, in an instant, who you were burns to ash & all
that remains is an unbound pillar of flame.

Later, you slowly remember there are things called words,
though they never mean what they did before you open
that door & return as a wild thing
barely contained
by your skin.

EVERYWHERE

everywhere I imagine
being alive, there you
are

& all I can do is say
thank you to a universe
that has you in it.

CONVINCING ARGUMENT

I just figured out
after all this time
that I love people
best when they
let me

& not when they
spend a lot of time
& energy trying
to convince me
it's not worth it.

Exact Thing

That moment you put
your hand on my arm?

How do I begin to tell
you that is the exact thing
that makes me love the
world so?

Remember This

You take my hand & say I want
to feel what's real & true with you

& suddenly, I'm standing there
in eternity, as if I'd never left

& to those of you who wonder
if Love is something you'll ever
trust again, I offer this: it is
how we remember
who we are.

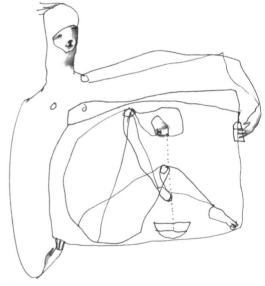

Whole Heart

I remember you saying
you were only interested
in my whole heart

& that's exactly what
I wanted to give

even if it might take
a few years to gather
up all the pieces from
the last time I tried
this whole heart thing.

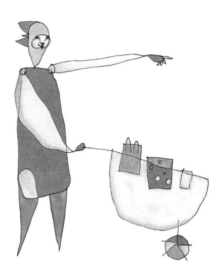

Clear Trail

Everywhere I go now
in the world, I see you
in the quiet looks between
people, as if you'd stopped
a moment before

to leave a trail of love
reminding me no matter
where I go, it leads me
back to you.

Two of Hearts

It has always been this way
from the moment I met you,

that even if the whole world
said no, there was nothing
that could stand in the way
of our hearts who were here
to say yes.

The Wonder of You

You ask if I see those parts
you still try to hide

& today, this is what I'd like
you to hear: I wanted all
of you from the very first &

I would not change a thing
about the wonder that is you.

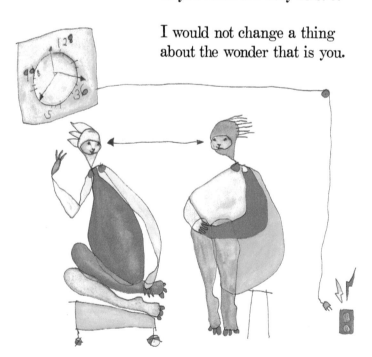

Light

There is a perfectly still moment right
before dawn, when the sun gathers itself

& then steps into the dark world & everything
is so filled with light that any doubts
from that long night are barely a memory.

It is the way of all things that
the night ends & the light returns.

The light always returns.

Happy Police

I have to be careful
on days I'm happy
to be alive

because where I live
there are too many
people who take it
personally

In The Night

In the night, sometimes I wake
to your hand on my chest &
I smile to myself & breathe
deeply

unwilling to move beyond that,
in case I disturb the perfect
arrangement of moments
that brought me here
to you.

Something Like Magic

I hope you know by now,
no matter where you are,
that the way Life sings
through us into the whole.
wide world is something
like magic

& you will always be
the reason I'm
not afraid
to love

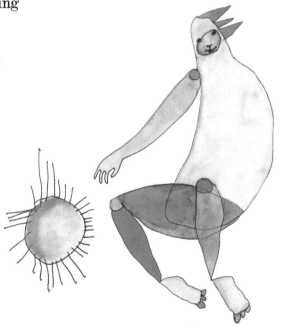

For all the thousand things
we do in the WORLd, I love
it best wheN We sit in
the SunLight Together,
smiling quietly with the Knowing
that Here is the perfect
plAce to be.

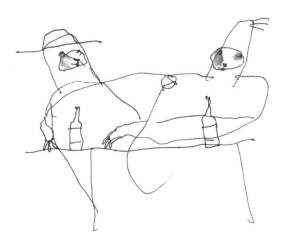

PERFECT PLACE

INVITATION OF THE DAY

There are times when I have no idea
what comes next & it's the thing I've
come to love most about being alive:

leaning in to hear the invitation
of each day & feeling my whole
body melt when I say
yes, yes, yes.

ON THE OTHER HAND

The trick to being alive is listening
to the part of me that uses no words,

because the part of me that uses words
is a little too dramatic for my own good.

I wake up every day now wanting
to tell people how the
WHOLE WORLD is
new since I found you
But MOST people are TOO BUSY
& they say Things Like THAT'S
NICE (yuk!). so I find I'M
spending more TIME with
CHILDREN & DOGS because
they listen to me get ALL excited
& then they Run around, too
Saying I know, I KNOW.

CHILDREN & DOGS

Help Wanted

One day, I decided to help
wherever I could

& it was almost like magic
because I was exactly
what the world needed
everywhere I went.

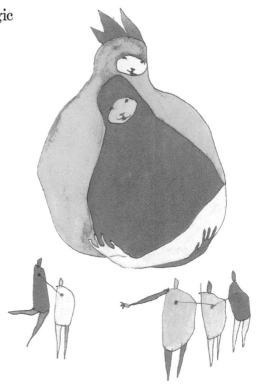

Early Morning

I never imagined back
when I thought I knew
so much about Love

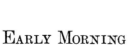

that I could sit here
silently in the early
morning with you &

the quiet would feed
something in me
all day long.

In that moment, our
eyes met & I remember
thinking THIS is what
it is to be STRUCK
by lightning, knowing
I would NEVER be
untouched by you again.

FIRST GLANCE

BALANCE OF POWER

The part of me that doubts
& the part of me that doesn't
seem to get along just fine

as long as
the part of me
that doubts
keeps it
to myself.

COME AS YOU ARE

The funny thing is you were
invited from the very beginning
& maybe you forgot. Or listened
to someone else who forgot.

But, just so you know, I'm going
to keep inviting you, again & again,
until you remember.

So, you might as well jump in now
with me & start living before it
gets out of hand.

Secret # 7:

You don't have to put up with anything. You CAN do something different.

Heart Lessons

I will carry you with me
to the end of my days

remembering all the
moments you taught me
to trust my own heart
to be alive

New Game

I see it in the way
you make yourself smaller,
so Life will not bump up
against you & it makes me
want to take your hand
& bring you out into the day
& say Let it touch you
& remember it's all
an excuse to Love.

During the times you feel most alone, I want you to remember this: I held you & Loved you from the Moment you came into this world & that's how it's always been for me & if you forget, I AM HERE to remind you as many times as you need.

REMEMBER

The Heart of You

There will be a time when you
will understand that there's nothing
in the heart of you to hide.

That even the dark waits for you
to let yourself shine clearly, because
even the dark remembers what
it was to be young,

before its passions were hidden
away & turned into something
you learned to fear.

Lead Away

Today, I'm ready to follow
my heart fully as long as
it's doing something fun
far away from most of
the people I know.

Right Time

Some days, I see how much
love you're holding back, waiting
for the right time, that it makes
me want to lean over & whisper
in your ear,

It's the right time.

My heart recognized
you from the very Beginning
& I knew it was only
a matter of time before
you stopped & recognized
mine, too.

A MATTER OF TIME

Sleeping Child

Someday, I hope you
have a child fall asleep
on your chest & in that
moment, with the soft
whisper of their breath
against your skin, I hope
you'll find the place
you've been looking for,
without any effort at all,
right there in your chest
where your child sleeps.

Quiet Songs

Even from far away, I still
feel you smile & my body
reaches for you without
thinking, singing songs
of love it knows that
you can hear.

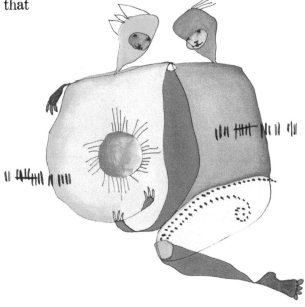

WILD SONGS

I wish for you a life
where your blood sings
with the voice of an
eager, wild thing.

With a voice that says
I am here

& in this short time,
this is the song I sing
because I can.

THE REASON WHY

We sat at the edge of the world
& you asked me to tell you why

& though a thousand things
came to mind, underneath them
all was a quiet voice saying,

Because you remind me of
everything there is in
this world to love.

OPEN ARMS

If you are lucky someday, you'll stand,
surrounded by people you know, or in
the dark of night, quietly by yourself
(it does not matter where exactly) &
Life will fill your whole self & it will
spill out a little with each breath you take
after that & you will give your promise to
hold the world safe, for as long as it takes

& then, afterwards, you'll go about your
days, wondering what has changed & you
won't see for a long time how it happens
in small moments.

When you smile at someone you do not
know. When you speak up, though it is
easier & quicker to just keep moving.
When you stop & hold the hand of a friend
who can no longer go on & you speak
in a low voice that only she can hear &
you say these words (or something
like them): I would not want to be
in a world without you in it.

& if you are lucky someday, maybe after
one of these moments, you'll understand
why Life filled your whole self & all you
could do was open your arms to hold the
world close & remember how to Love.

Reasons for Tea

There are so many reasons
I love you that I think
we should sit here over tea

& I'll tell you a few
every day, for the rest
of our lives.

First Time

Each morning, I breathe
in the whole world again
like it's the very first time

& remember that all the
words we use about being
alive aren't the same
as Life itself.

There is a Strength
that comes from
KNOWing you will
die & still refusing
to Love with anything
less than your
whole Self.

Anything Less

Favorite Days

We sat at the edge of the world
& you laughed & asked a thousand
questions

& later, at dusk, I carried you sleeping
in my arms & you woke for a moment
& smiled & said Today was my favorite

& I said Shhh, but I had to agree.

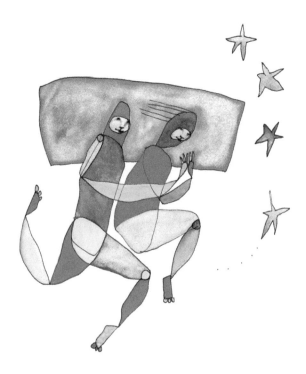

First Things

If I had known everything
I know about who you are
back when I didn't know
a thing about you

I would've pulled you aside
sooner & said Thank you
for being one of the most
incredible people I will
ever know.

Business Dress

I watch you sitting
in the morning sun

& there is such stillness
it takes my breath away

& I wonder how we
ever forget we are
exactly how Love looks
as we quietly go about
this business of living.

One Decision

It takes awhile
to see this, but
there's only one
hard decision
you have to
make:

will you trust
your own heart
to lead?

& that will give you
your whole life

no matter what
you decide.

Next Move

You wonder what it'd be
like to be loved for everything
you are & I want to take
your face in my hands
& say, You already are.

Now, you just have to
remember to feel it.

Happiness

I love it when people ask me
to tell them my secret for
being happy because I don't
really have a secret, other than:

1. I don't think the universe is
   out to get me.

2. I don't listen very long to
   people who want to convince
   me that I should be unhappy

3. I pay attention to things that
   make me unhappy & I stop
   doing them as soon as possible.

That's pretty much the whole secret.

Secret #8:

This world is Amazing & you'll forget that again & again your whole life. But if you Remember more than you forget, You'll be fine.

Say yes. Whatever it is,
say yes with your WHOLE
HEART & simple as it sounds
that's ALL the excuse Life
Needs to GRAB you by the
hands & start to DANCE.

PRODIGAL CHILD

For a long time, I held to the knowledge
that I was a child of the earth, raised on rich soil
& air the flavor of dark bread

& though I heard about the sea, those stories
were whispered & strange & far from the ones
I knew.

Then, I met you, with eyes the color of storms,
or the emerald of deep waves when sunlight
moves across your face &

you are such a liquid invitation to the world
that I wonder now if the sea has called to me
my whole life & hearing nothing in return

sent you here to bring me home.

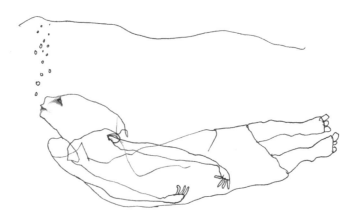

LAST WORD

This is probably
a good time to say
something profound

& I probably would, if
I believed words could
do that,

but words that sound
profound are often
lies.

Because the most
profound things
about living are
felt & require

no words at all.

a note from kai

I've been telling stories & speaking about creativity & making art for over 40 years
now. Strangely enough, it took me almost that whole time to see what my work is
all about. That every moment is a gift of Love.

It feels to me like now is another one of those times we need to hear that clearly. That
Love truly is all there is. It's actually been more difficult for me to understand this
than you might think, mainly because I've been writing about stuff like this for a long
time & I was pretty sure I already knew it. Then my whole life changed. I won't lie; it
was more difficult than I ever imagined. But that's what it took for me to remember.

So, it turned out to be one of my favorite things ever. Because now I don't have
to pretend to know anything & I get to look & wonder & listen all over again.

This is the book that comes out of remembering & finding Love again in the world.
Think of it as an invitation to remember your own laughter & play & connection
that weaves through every moment of your life. Pull up a comfy chair & join in.
I'm glad you're here...

about flying edna

flying edna is a small company. Two artists & a dog. Everything we write, create,
& teach is about experiencing interconnectedness & cultivating the practice
of presence. It's about going towards a life you love. Which is why, in our own
studio, we choose environmentally conscious practices & work with sustainable
materials we find from fellow makers & vendors who share our respect for the
planet.

Since meeting in 2015, Fia, Kai & Yoshi have journeyed together through 45
states, temporarily making their home in the Midwest, Maine, Montana & now
Cape Cod. By the time you read this, they may be off on another journey, but
you can always find them at flyingedna.com

CPSIA information can be obtained
at www.ICGtesting.com
Printed in the USA
JSHW050425270323
39485JS00015B/313

9 780998 149028